Adventures of the Acropolis marbled girls

Eleni Hadjoudi-Toynta

Adventures of the Acropolis marbled girls

*A true story that took place
on the rock of the Acropolis*

Illustrations: Spyros Gousis

AGYRA
publications

Translated from Greek into English
Eugene Hadjoudis

Text editor: Kiriaki Papakonstantinou
BA English Language & Literature / MA Psycholinguistics / DIPTRANS - DPSI
Chartered Linguist (Translator) / Translators - Interpreters Trainer
Member of the Chartered Institute of Linguists in London

Cover Design: Efthimis Dimoulas

© 2012 ELENI HADJOUDI-TOUNTA &
D.A. PAPADIMITRIOU S.A. «AGYRA» Publications
271 L. Katsoni str. •Ag. Anargiroi P.O. 135 62 Athens, Greece
Tel.: +30 210 2693800-4 - Fax: +30 210 2693806-7
e-mail agyra@agyra.gr • www.agyra.gr

ISBN: 978-960-547-006-7

*To Melina Mercouri, and Zisis Sotiriou,
chief guardian of Acropolis, because both of them,
although they lived in different centuries,
struggled, each one in his own way, so that
the marbles of Parthenon, return to their home.*

I' ll tell you a true short story, more like a tale, and therefore it will start just like any other tale.

Once upon a time, one evening, something strange happened on the Acropolis. It happened where the temple of Parthenon, Erechtheion with the Caryatids and the Temple of Athena Nike stand. However, I'll not tell you about all of them, but just for the Caryatids, and the time they talked to Zisis, the guardian of Acropolis and entrusting their great secret to him.

From ancient times, stories presented them as six marbled princesses who lived there, on the rock of Acropolis. People remembered that the figures of these fairy ladies were curved with care and love on Pentelic marble by some famous and great sculptors.

So Caryatids were standing there, centuries after centuries, in serene and cherished at the back side of the Temple of Erechtheas, the first King of Athens. They were standing arched and proud bearing baskets on their head, like some escort in honor of the King.

Suddenly, everything changed and out of the six Caryatids only five remained. And they stayed there, on the Acropolis, incurable nostalgic for their sixth little sister, the one that Lord Elgin abducted, together with many other statues and reliefs of the Parthenon.

Ever since, many summers and winters have passed and the Caryatids continued to stay in the same place, calm despite such disaster, with the hope depicted on their sweet faces, and this is because they had a big secret. They kept it deeply in their hearts, and this secret kept them hoping – hoping and dreaming that some day, their beloved little sister will be back to them:

"It is impossible not to come back", the five little sisters kept saying to each other in the nights when they were alone and nobody could hear them.

Because, believe me, Caryatids had a warm heart, just like a mother's bosom. They always talked for the one they lost. They even talked for the old times, when they were all together, joyful and happy. But, above all, they talked for the future and asked themselves in deep sor-

row and nostalgia: "Will she ever come back again? Can it be we see her again?"

One day, however, there came the fall, with freshness playing on the grass, Caryatids thought that the miracle happened and their little sister came back to them. It was early in the morning when they saw the workers holding her in their arms and with some high scaffolds reaching the empty space and putting her there.

But the heavenly happiness did not last long, because they saw the forgery. No! The one that took their place was not their little sister. They got angry, but they took care to play it cool, so that nobody could understand that they had not a good eye for the stranger who replaced their beloved one. The one brought from England by lord Guilford and put in Her place, in order to fill the empty space.

The five little sisters wondered, for were those who made her: "How they could think it was possible this alien without a soul, without any

pulse, with a cold body, without any breath, and a face without the illuminating breeze of Her be next to them!"

They never revealed they were unhappy having next to them a false one, a forged one, a "counterfeit", because something inside them was telling them that:

"Things might have come this way, but they wouldn't go on like this".

Actually, Zisis, the guardian of Acropolis, called her "Kalpouzana". Caryatids have seen him a lot of times standing in front of them talking to the alien:

"E! Kalpouzana[1], poor one, you will also be suffering far form your own people. However, the time will come and you will go back in your country and the emigrant back to us".

When Zisis was young, he was called *"the brave one of Olympus"* because as a fearless lad had fought on Olympus Mountain and Chalcidice[2], when our country, years ago, was enslaved to the Turks.

Zisis, as soon as he learned that Greeks went uprising for their freedom, came to fight for Greece. He arrived from Pest, the capital of Hungary, where he was living and working as a merchant. He sold all his holdings and offered all his money to the struggle of the nation.

When the great uprising came to an end and the Turks left Greece, Zisis sold his house in order to give the money to the country, which was very poor after four hundred years of slavery. Destruction, however, has left its signs everywhere: houses, animals, the environment, the monuments. On the Acropolis, both Greek and foreign archeologists and workers were trying to find and put to place all the marbles that have been buried under the ruins following the catastrophe. Zisis also went to Acropolis and asked the director of the excavation to make him a guardian, since he was homeless and jobless.

---

1 Kalpouzana: Counterfeit.
2 Chalcidice: District of Northern Greece.

"With all my respect to your person, mister Director, I would like to serve as a guardian of the Acropolis. I will help to turn down all the Turkish houses and mosques that have been erected on the rock".

The director, mister Pittakis, had already heard many good things about Zisis from important people and he knew about his love for the country. However, he was astonished when Zisis told him:

"And I want you to know, mister Director, that I don't want to take a full salary. Half of it I'll leave to the state for the war treasury".

Ever since that day, Zisis became not a simple guardian of Acropolis, but chief guardian of the antiquities. This was his official job. During the day, like a true guardian as he was, he was patrolling around the area of Acropolis keeping his eyes wide open on both foreigners and Greek visitors, who were going around to see and admire the temples and ancient statues. Actually he did not allow anyone to touch them. He didn't allow even any piece of earth to be taken in their palms. The good guardian kept always saying "no" to this and "no" to that: "You can admire as much as you want our monuments, but you should not touch them. They have suffered enough", he used to say to the visitors of Acropolis.

And he was able to converse amply with the foreigners, as he was fluent in French and German. He could also speak Hungarian, Italian and Turkish, since he was born at Servia of Kozani, Greece, during the enslavement of the country.

When the visitors and other guardians were leaving and no soul remained on the rock, he used to go close to his beloved "daughters", as he called the Caryatids. They were his company. He was confessing his grief, as well as his reasonable and unreasonable complaints to them. He was also telling his "daughters" all the wrongdoings that had taken place on and around the Acropolis.

"Did you see, my little daughters, what happened today with those two German archeologists? I talked to them about a lot of things, for the life of Athens and my own. When they understood that I like to read history, they gave me as a present the book they had. Here it is, look at it, I have it in my hands; it is the history of Herodotus".

The Caryatids kept watching him proud and silent, since the statues stay always still and dumb. Zisis, the guardian, however, continued to narrate old stories every day, without any hesitation. He had great patience, because he loved them so much. He knew that some day they could speak to him. A lot of times, he was singing to his "daughters".

In joy I keep playing
With my six girls, saying
Each one a full word
To be spelled to the world.

On finishing one song, Zisis the guardian chose another one:

Ducks and geese on sea side trunks
Partridges at river banks
Is there water at your sink
For my daughter come and drink
Wash her hair and maiden pink
Then get dressed up in a blink
Going for a walk I think.

And suddenly, one evening Spring was in the air, with myrtles, poppies and lilies among the rocks of Acropolis, when Zisis, the guardian, run to his "daughters".

"Today, my little girls, you have been admired by those three Americans, who are important and famous scientists. They were admiring you continually and expressed enthusiastically:

15

'These girls are mostly beautiful! Their body is a source of joy and they seem to breathe under their cloths. How loosely and marvelously their long hair is combed; and what gently caress their sweet faces!' these important visitors kept saying as they were observing you, my little girls. Then, they turned to me as I was watching them:

'We, in America, we have gold, you here in Greece, you have something more important than our gold. You have ancient statues and temples. We are coming from so far away only to see them'. Hear what else they told me, my little girls: That I care for you, that I am a good guardian". Yet, neither that day, had Caryatids spoken to him.

On another occasion, he told them his misfortune with his Psaris, the donkey.

"I had a great emotion yesterday noon! As I was taking my Psaris to have him shoed, he was scared when a dog jumped in front of him. Frightened, he fell on a freshly planted small tree and uprooted it.

I jumped before Psaris, he was going to throw me down. I waited a while, so the poor donkey could relax and then we went to the Town Hall. I had to repair the damage. I talked to an employee in order to keep from my salary the amount necessary in order to plant another tree. He looked at me amazed, moving his head:

'My man, are you feeling good? You are going to pay since nobody saw you doing something? My good man, goodbye!'

With all this talking and chatting, even as the Caryatids remained silent all these years, they were convinced that he was a good man and, above all, how much he loved them. That is why they trusted him and decided to talk to him. Because statues have this charisma: When they know that someone really loves them, then yes, they will talk to him. And don't think they have a high voice, like people do. No, their voice is more like a whisper, and can be heard only by those having tender hearts.

And this day it was different when Caryatids talked to Zisis, the guardian. Strange things have happened before: He was slipping, as every day, in the wooden small house, standing by the entrance of the Acropolis and which was used also as a guardhouse. It was still early in the morning, when a strange noise made him get out of bed.

Frogs were quarrelling with the larks, and his dog, Gikas, was sleeping embraced with his cat, while his turtle had grown ears! Zisis the guardian saw all these things and could not believe in his eyes. "Great Lord, something else, something different will happen today", raved Zisis, the guardian.

All right, after washing himself, he put on his white fustanella[3], his dark modern Greek sandals and his red fez; he had some olives with tea, and he ascended to open the entrance for the visitors of the Acropolis. Four or five French people arrived this day. Actually they talked to him and they were amazed that he knew so well their language. In the evening, on closing the gates and after he made sure no one had remained on the Acropolis, he run to his "daughters". He sat on the same rock that he used to sit every day, just in front of them. He filled his long tobacco pipe and stared at them. And, as he used to

---

3. Fustanella: A traditonal Greek kilt.

tell them the things that happened the previous day, he started again:

"Yesterday, March the twenty fifth, I went to Agia Eirini. King Othon with Queen Amalia was also there. They arrived in a coach made of glass, being pulled by four white horses. You don't speak to me, my daughters? Tell me something, after all, why are you so proud and disdainful? Every day, be it rain, be it snows with heat or cold, I am coming to talk to you. Even I told you the reason of my engagement resolution when I was young. You should have understood by now how much I love you". And, Zisis, the guardian, started singing.

Send me a word, my dear
when you will talk to me, sincere
to cover mounts up with rose beds
and plains in hues of reds.

He was about to finish his song when he heard a sweet whisper all around. It was like the sound of a butterfly, as she jumps from flower to flower.

"Zisis, our dear guardian, from this day we cease our silence. We are going to talk to you, however, all together in one voice, except the Kalpouzana, as you call her, because she does not know our language and she has not pentelic blood in her veins. However, we love her. Alas, if you knew, our good guardian, how great our grief is for our little sister in the foreign land! There is not a single minute passing by without us thinking of her. We endured all these years of separation because we have a great secret. For years now, our good guardian, we live in the agony and the shadow of our secret. Today, however, we will share it with you, because you are worth of it".

Zisis was surprised. He could not believe his ears. He was tongue-tied. Was it true? His "daughters" were talking to him? But, yes, it was true. They were talking to him. He quickly overcame the astonishment and said:

"At last, my daughters! I knew that one day you would trust me. I am all ears to hear your sweet voice and your secret".

"So, this terrible day, our good guardian Zisis", the Caryatids continued whispering, "when the abduction of our little sister took place by the English lord, our country was not yet free from slavery. Up here, between Erechtheion and Parthenon, the Turkish commanders of the fortress had built their houses and lived with their families. They have turned the Acropolis into a fortress. They called it the Castle. The day that the damage happened, we saw the English talking with the Turk agha, showing him all the ornaments of the Parthenon. We felt that

21

something terrible was going to happen. After a while, we saw workers with scaffolds, hammers, axes and sows, going up and dismantling them one by one. We shed tears, because the pain we felt was great, since all the figures that they were taking away were standing for centuries intact, exactly in front of us, keeping us company. The workers of the English Lord were working for many months, until they detached as many pieces as they could. And then, oh! Then, Zisis, our good guardian, it was the time of our little sister. First they were discussing to take us all together. Then, nobody knows what happened and they took only one. Oh! If you can imagine, Zisis, our good guardian, our suffering when they dropped her down to earth; while she was lying down, until her abduction, we filled the air with sobbing and tears. We could hear our little sister saying:

'Who knows, my dearest, if we will see each other again. I don't want to be taken away from you. I don't want to lose our golden sun and our beautiful sky'.

We were crying all together, Zisis, our good guardian, we were crying so loud, that the valet of Disdari – as the Turks called the commander of the Castle – Abdoulah, went away in order not to listen to our crying".

"Ah! My little girls, if we have not been liberated, who knows which foreign museum you were going to decorate!" said Zisis the guardian, with sorrow.

"Maybe you are right, our good guardian. However, the same night of the abduction all the stars of the sky were gathered above our heads and were crying for this injustice. But, Zisis, our good guardian, a little boy was crying with us too. He was no more than eight years old. They called him Kerim, a little Turk, who loved us. Especially our abducted little sister. On the side where she stood in Erechtheion, there was a big rock. Kerim used to climb up that rock and touch her fingertips. Kerim, ever since he was born, because he was born up here, his house was next to us, he kept coming to play nearby and used to talk to us. His mother, Zeinep, used to bring him up here when he was still a baby, and played with him in the small rock which lies just below our legs. 'Look, look, Kerim, look the girls, how they are looking to you, how much they love you, Kerim'.

"You should not speak to him at all, my little daughters. He was an enemy", Zisis the guardian interrupted them.

"No, our good guardian. We had to. He was a little boy. We talked to him when we felt that we were his company and he loved us. We asked him only to tell nothing to anybody. He kept his word. He never, but never, said anything to anybody. Thus Kerim used to come to us sometimes joyful, some other times frown and tell us about his grand mother, Dede, as he called her, giving him cookies, or complaining for his brothers, because they were beating him. Some other times Kerim was coming shining clean, compared to other days, but with a sad face. It was the days when he went down with his family to the Turkish baths, the Hamam, as the Turks called it, in order to have a bath. It was near Aerides, in Plaka. Kerim could not, as he told us, get used the

24

etching in his eyes. He was crying endlessly. That is why, after each visit at the Hamam, Kerim was sulky. In a few words, Zisis, our good guardian, the day the boy saw one little sister uprooted and thrown down to earth he burst out in strong weeping, stronger than ours. The following days he used to come every few minutes and asked. "When will the girl be back?" We promised him that she will definitely be back one day. However, in a few days, his father, who was the commander of the Castle, was ordered to return to Constantinople and was replaced by somebody else. Thus, Kerim left at noon, after coming to us to say good-by and caress the empty space of our little sister.

Thus the winter passed by – which was a heavy one that year. Summer arrived, hot and calm and winter once again. But one day, something different, something strange happened in the sky. A little sun, deep red, with green light was wandering above our heads.

'Ah! A red dwarf', we said immediately for the little sun. So we baptized it, 'red dwarf'. For an unexplained reason, this morning, Zisis, our good guardian, nor a Turkish soldier, neither Disdaris nor anyone from their families that lived up here was going to wake up. Calm and absolute quietness dominated. We were observing this little red sun, until we noticed that it reached very close to us and stopped between Parthenon and Erechtheion. We observed carefully this strange visitor, the 'red dwarf'. We examined it and then we noticed that on it there was a small creature. It was so small, like a seed of grape. Although it was so small, it was the shape of a little girl with blond curls waving in the air. The green light was shining on the small face with its little blue eyes. She moved her little hands and with a sweet warm voice, told us:

'Don't be surprised, beautiful girls; we will not share our great secret with anybody else. Whatever we say, it will stay among us. I arrived with the small sun, in order not to awake the people of the Castle, and thus hear our secret. I saw from up there that night the misfortune that happened down there. But it was not possible to come that time. I had first to find your little sister, in order to bring her message to you. I want to stop your suffering. I like to see you smiling and give you

hope. I'll be your messenger. I can transfer every message to your fairy little sister'.

At first, Zisis, our good guardian, we were confused, frightened; then all of us in one voice asked: 'You bring a message? A message from our little sister, good little girl? Tell us, oh, tell us, where is she? Is she well? Does she think of us?'

'Your little sister', continued the little creature 'is enclosed in a big museum in London, together with all other ornaments from the Parthenon. A lot of people see and admire her, and the faces of Dias, Hermes, Demeter, Ares, Athena, and Hephaestus the beautiful horse-

men who accompanied in honor the Panathenea festivity. I saw all of
them a bright night talking to each other. The Museum was filled with
Greek voices. They are united and cherished like the fingers on your
hands'.

'Good girl, please, tell us more about our misfortunate little sister'.

'She feels loneliness and nostalgic, as happens with the rest of the
marbles', said the little girl. 'She thinks of you day and night. She is
trapped, however, like a partridge in the trap. She wants to be near
you again. She does not like to get old in a terrible wet place. I have
also seen the spots she already has from parasites, since she lives without any sun and light in this foreign country. She is crying each time
she remembers you. But, she does something very pleasant in order to
keep hoping'.

'Please, tell us what she is doing? Please, tell us, good little girl', we
begged her.

29

The little creature stared at us and continued. 'The still nights, she travels with her mind. She comes back to the roads of Attica and visits Eleonas[4], she hears the sound of sea-waves coming from Sounion. She talks with you and enjoys the shining sun on her face. This way, she feels happy and hopeful'.

'Ah, good and beautiful little girl. What a big heart! You gave us great happiness by coming with your sun in order to bring us the message from our little sister, our little spark – we call her like this, because she is like a spark inside our heart – so that to encourage and give us hope for life. Go back and tell her that we dream to see her little face again, and our ears would like to hear her refreshing voice. Tell her not to forget the sunset, the fresh breeze of Hymettus[5], caressing her beautiful little face. Tell her, also, our sweet girl, to be proud. Her beauty, together with the other marbles of Parthenon, which decorate this foreign Museum, is the reason that thousands of people are acquainted and admire the ancient Greek art. Sometime, all these people will understand that our little sister should be back'.

'But you are not afraid to awake the guardian and kill you?'

'No, I am not afraid at all'.

'How is that?' we asked the little creature.

'I have power on me', told us.

_____

4. Eleonas: Olive tree grove.
5. Hymettus: Mount of Attica, near Athens.

'And where do you hide this power, our good little girl?'

'It is not hidden. It is my own eyes', she answered.

'And what you can do with your eyes?'

'In case of danger, I can stare at those threatening me and disarm them. Then, I can surround them with flowers. Only flowers, many flowers; so many that they could be drown by their perfume!'

'Tell us something else, little girl, when you will be down on Earth?'

'Seventy moons are needed until I'll be down', answered the creature. 'But that time I will arrive together with Alkyoni, the brightest star, in order to bring the joyful news. Then numerous poppies will blossom on earth. Ships full of life will cross seas and oceans, while flutes, harps, pipes, clarinets, flutes, drums, violins, guitars and trumpets, will sound in such a way that human ears never heard. Boys and girls decorated like valleys, like forests, like seas, will lead the dance, with such a youthful vigor and charm, that human eyes have never seen before. Goodbye, beautiful girls, wait for me. Count the moons'.

'Goodbye, good little girl, goodbye, we will wait for you, we will be counting the moons'.

'One more thing, before you go away, tell us your name!'

'My name is Melina, goodbye and do not forget to count the moons'.

'Yes, we will be counting the moons, sweet little girl'.

This is our great secret, Zisis, our good guardian. It is the hope and promise that the blond little girl gave us, as she was riding the red dwarf".

This long conversation, however, brought the morning light. Cocks started their symphony. Zisis, the guardian, confused with what he had heard, remained speechless. His heart beating like a drum almost burst into pieces. Have the Caryatids spoken to him? Was it true? He heard well? Was he awake? Or he has seen the sweetest dream of his life? Whatever it was, he has enjoyed it. He left the Caryatids thoughtful. He wanted to do something. He was full of ambition. He liked to help in his own way as well, so that all the ornaments of Parthenon would be back together with his other "girl", the one in the foreign land. He liked it. How much he liked it! But how?

Here it is! The chance appeared immediately. Next morning, he was informed by the Archeological Society, that an important foreigner was going to visit Athens and the Acropolis in one month. In a few days, he learned that the exceptional visitor was Prince Eduard of England, the son of Queen Victoria, the successor to the throne. He was travelling with "Serapes". This was the name of Eduard's frigate.

Ever since that day, Zisis the guardian lost his sleep. He was thinking all day long what he could do. And suddenly his mind lightened. His mustache reached his ears from his smile...

That's it! How he had not thought of it before? A letter! He was going to write a letter and deliver it to the prince, with a request to the King, to exercise his power, so that the uprooted Caryatids to return home. And not only that; In the letter he was going to put the request all the garments of Parthenon, which the workers of the English Lord had violently sawed, be back as well. The fact that he didn't know the language of the prince was not a problem. He was going to find the

wise man Kambouroglou. He knew his house, in Plaka, near the Church of Agia Sotira. He knew and the hours he would be there.

Mister Gregoris Kampouroglou was a famous journalist – a famous and very busy man. This was the reason he was working during hours not usual to common people. He was sleeping at eight o'clock in the evening and was awake at two o'clock after midnight, writing endlessly.

So, Zisis waited until sundown, mounted his donkey Psaris and directed him to the house of mister Kambouroglou. He found the open-hearted white haired, wise journalist among piles of papers and books. On seeing Zisis entering his office, he asked:

"How was this good thing to remember me, Zisis?"

"I am always thinking of you, mister Gregoris. But what can I do? I have to guard the marbles, above all. Do I interrupt you from your writings?"

Mister Kambouroglou, although he had not finished the article he was writing for the next day's edition of the journal he was cooperating with, immediately stopped his work in order to hear what Zisis wanted. After all, he estimated and loved him very much. Therefore, he asked.

"Tell me, Zisis, what is going on?"

"You know better than me, mister Gregoris, we are expecting Prince Eduard of England to arrive at Athens on Wednesday. He will visit the Acropolis as well".

"I know it, Zisis, and I'll also be up there, because I have to write about this visit".

"Then well, mister Gregoris, I would like you to write for me a letter in his language. In this, I'll be asking him, when he becomes a King to take care so that all the marbles of Acropolis return home, all these that lord Thomas Elgin Bruce abducted".

Mister Kambouroglou could not believe his ears, such a daring act!

"Is it wise what you are asking, Zisis? You believe the English will give back the marbles so easy? They have them in their Museum and thousands of people pay every day in order to admire them. How can this be done? I think it is extremely difficult, if not impossible".

Zisis the guardian, however, continued pressing mister Kambouroglou to write the letter. He pressed him even more.

"I insist, Mister Gregoris, to write it. Otherwise, I will write it in French".

Thus, Mister Kambouroglou, at Zisis persistence started writing the letter.

When he finished, he stood up from his velvet armchair, gave the letter to Zisis and wished the courageous and optimist patriot good luck.

On his return back, as Zisis was riding his donkey, like feeling the joyful beating of his heard, begun to run in the narrow streets of Plaka, knocking his legs sharing the joy of his rider.

Zisis went in Psaris's ear and murmured. "Be careful, Psaris; do not be foolhardiness. It was not such a long time ago that I jumped down from your back, and who knows how many bones I saved that time. So, go ahead easy in your way and stop your vivacity".

With all these going on, Zisis the guardian was marching and day dreaming, the day that he was going to hand the letter to Prince Eduard. And this day duly arrived.

It was a spring morning with fresh flower smells all around. The blue sky and all the hills around were welcoming the important foreigner and his escort. Zisis, the guardian, *"the grandfather of Olympus"* as they called him now that his hair was white, like the snow of Olympus mountain, for this day he was dressed in his official fustanella with the one hundred slantings. He welcomed Prince Eduard at the entrance of the Acropolis. He gently saluted and guided him and his followers to the Propylea and the other monuments. Then, he retreated behind them and followed at a distance the guidance of the Greek and foreign archaeologists. The archaeologists explained and gave answers to the prince and his friends, since they were full of questions.

"What is this and what is that, and what about the others?" Zisis was waiting full of agony for the crucial moment. He was holding carefully the precious envelope in his hands. More than two hours had already passed and there was no sign that the questions would come to an end.

But, yes, at last! The agony reached an end. They all started descending the Rock. Then, Zisis approached Eduard courageously saying:

"Please, your Excellency, accept this letter of mine. I hope you will find the time to read it carefully. It is for the good of my country". Eduard was puzzled; yet, he kept the enigmatic envelope. And when all the officials left and Zisis, the guardian, was left alone, he kneeled down, looked at the sky and thanked God for enabling him to take such action for his country.

After that, he ran to the Caryatids, to tell them the good news.

"Maybe, it can be done; maybe he will understand the wrong thing, the injustice made to the Parthenon taking all his ornaments. The evil they did to you. Maybe now they change and became different people, with a different attitude. Let us hope that they will return her, since they were made to living all together under the sun and the clear sky of Greece, and they are 'our pride, our sacrifices, they are our name; it is our History'".

As Zisis the guardian was talking to Caryatids, a dream powder covered him and he saw the marbles standing at their place, as in the days of their glory. He saw real Gods holding young children by their hand and strolling down,

on earth. He saw Byzantine
saints, heroes of the Greek
War of Independence, kind-heart-
ed people smiling happily. He saw most
beautiful girls, ornamented to collect lilies
around of the world and handsome boys pin-
ning up bright moons in the girls' hair. So many
things were what the *"grand-father of Olympus"*
saw. Sky high, a panorama of stars was shining in
multicoloured silvery reflections.

However, one star from the crowd, the one in the middle,
the most shining one, distinguished. It looked like smiling and waving
at him, something like a promise to come down to earth soon, in order

also to help for the return of the marbles. Thousands of falling stars surrounded him and he arrived at the field of paradise, Zisis, the guardian. He walked on the seaweed of the sky. He listened to the seraphim playing harmonica and his soul was full of light, colour and music. It was then when he started the singing:

> *Oh! When the spring*
> *is here at last*
> *And birds come back anew*
> *And flowers, as once, outlast*
> *As times before,*
> *I'll wait for you.*

> *As summer once again*
> *comes through*
> *On mistral from the shore,*
> *As times before,*
> *I'll wait for you*

> *But when the fall*
> *sets in accrue*
> *and humid weather*
> *makes its coup*
> *and clouds cover me all anew,*
> *I'll come and find you;*
> *won't wait for you...*

And then, I will ask:

> *Oh! Star, my little star*
> *What your mandates are?*

We would like to thank Melina's Mercuri foundation and especially Mrs. Emmanuella Pavlidi, for Melina's photograph.

The Little girl

Melina Mercouri, the sweet, little girl who came with her sun, even before her birth, in order to give courage and hope to the Caryatids and promised to come down to earth to assist towards the return of the sculptures of Parthenon and all other Greek antiquities, kept her promise. She arrived midsummer and marked with her presence the cultural and political life of the country. She appeared like a shining star and illuminated the whole world. She obliged the world to discuss again and again the request of Greece, to have the sculptures of the Parthenon returned to the land which created them.

All Greeks are aware of Melina's inexhaustible fight. As Minister of Culture, she never stopped making efforts to influence Presidents, other Ministers, and Members of Parliament, Philhellenes and, in general, officials of foreign countries, in order to show interest and support her vision. Today the "Melina Mercouri Foundation" Supports her will concerning the founding of the New Museum of Acropolis, in which a specific space will be kept empty for the great day when the marbles of the Parthenon come back home. And if, as we all hope, Melina's efforts have a positive result, then Melina will be reborn – something she herself had said – and participate in the festivities along with the rest of us for the realization of her vision.

Melina's dream was fulfilled in 2009 with the Acropolis Museum Inauguration, in which empty space is kept for the great day. And everybody knows that she will be watching, riding a red dwarf, to see the placing of the marbles in their place.

Melina,
"I know that the joyful mandate will some day arrive...
All sweet like the fruits of olive tree...
Dressed all in green and clouds...!"
I'll be waiting for you...

We would like to thank Mr. Manos Haritatos for allowing us to photocopy Zisis Sotiriou's sketch from the rich Ε.Λ.Ι.Α. library.

The Chief guard of the Greek antiquities

Zisis Sotiriou was born in the Turkish occupied Servia of Kozani (Creece), in the beginning of the 19th century. Until he was sixteen years old he lived in Servia. He had good teachers, as his family was well off. Foreign languages, history and mathematics were his favorable subjects.

When he was sixteen years old, he left for Hungary because, as he used to say, he could not stand seeing his country enslaved. He returned when his country needed help in order to fight for the liberation.

He lived in Athens until the end of his life, sending incessantly letters to kings, princes, and ambassadors of foreign countries and benefactors of Greece. His anxiety and big desire in all these letters was always the same: "To bring back all the marbles of the Acropolis". The same was also subject of the letter he handed to Prince of Wales, when in May 1862 he visited the Acropolis. This letter was first published in the French magazine *"National Graphic Review"*, in 1877. Editor of the magazine was the French Philhellene, Professor Alexander Meymar.

Of course, Zisis Sotiriou vision was not fulfilled while he was still in life, nor during the life of Eduard VII, the Prince of Wales (1901-1910), who was later the King of England.

Contemporary Greeks, however, believe that we will have the chance – due to the inexhaustible campaign of Melina Mercouri and her deserving companion and Philhellene, Jules Dassin, who worked all his life, as well as all the British Philhellenes, who founded The British Committee for the returning of the marbles of Parthenon – to see them in the new Museum of Acropolis since they are the symbol of the world civilization and culture.